The Best Cook

A Division of The McGraw-Hill Companies

Columbus, Ohio

www.sra4kids.com

SRA/McGraw-Hill

*A Division of The **McGraw·Hill** Companies*

Send all inquiries to:
SRA/McGraw-Hill
8787 Orion Place
Columbus, OH 43240-4027

ISBN 0-07-569787-4
    3 4 5 6 7 8 9 DBH 05 04 03 02

My mom is a good cook.
My dad is a better cook.

Mom works hard at cooking.
She took cooking lessons.

Dad never took cooking lessons.
He has cooked all his life.

Mom has lots of cookbooks.
She made a wooden bookcase for them.

Dad uses cookbooks a little bit.
Last night, he stood on a cookbook
to get a pan from a hook.

Mom saves cooking tips in a wooden box.
Dad saves cooking tips in his head.
Mom is a good cook, but Dad is the best.